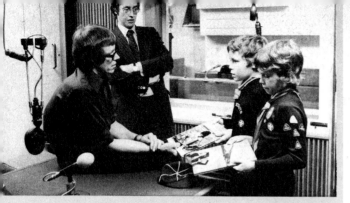

Last year's Cub Scout Annual was a sell-out! And it was read by people other than Cub Scouts . . . David Rider, who presents 'Playground' (Radio One's Magazine Programme for younger listeners) showed an interest in both the Cub Scout and the Scout Annuals, so Graham Clark (4th Boreham Wood Cub Scout Pack) and Wayne Gregory (22nd Hampstead Sea Scout Troop) went along to the BBC's Studios with Geoff Platt (Assistant General Editor of The Scout Association) to present David Rider with copies of the Annuals.

photograph by Jack Olden.

THE CUB SCOUT annual 1978

Scouts The Official Annual of The Scout Association

Edited by David Harwood

Published in Great Britain by
World Distributors (Manchester) Limited,
A Member of the Pentos Group,
P.O. Box 111, 12 Lever Street, Manchester M60 1TS.

Printed in Great Britain by Jarrold & Sons Ltd., Norwich.

SBN 7235 0429 6

The Cover photographs

(front) Up! Up! And Away! Cub Scouts watch the lift-off of the National Scout Air Activities Centre's hot air balloon.

With their feet firmly on the ground of the Buffalo Lawn at Gilwell Park, the outside broadcast unit from Thames Television record a programme for **Magpie** . . . you'll find the story of this television programme in the feature which starts on page 12.

(back) Cub Scouts certainly get out and about! Using a public telephone and stalking are just two of the many things they can do.

photographs by Lawrence D. Curtis and David Harwood.

This Annual belongs to:

£1.35

T HE most important thing in the world to young Stan Summers was his rabbit. Belle was a real beaut, with the longest, silkiest ears that any rabbit ever had. Her big brown eyes glowed red whenever she saw Stan and her nose wiggled a welcome to him. She was so tame she could really have been let loose like a dog, but it was a crowded terraced street and she was safest living in a hutch in the back yard.

Tonight Stan was tempted to take her indoors with him for company. She'd be perfectly good in the kitchen, and the two kids didn't dare mess her about. But he was in charge, just for tonight, and he supposed he'd be too busy to talk to Belle, what with getting the kids to bed and looking after Mum.

Dad was on night shift and Mum was ill in bed.

"So you're the boss, young Stan," Dad had said before he went. "Keep the kids quiet and look after your Mum."

And Mum, from her bed in the front room where she was sleeping until she was well again, had called out: "Our Stan'll manage fine. Not to worry, Dad!"

Stan wasn't worried either. He'd often helped with Fred and Alfie, and Mum was getting better now. She just had to be kept quiet, the Doctor had said.

So Stan gave the kids their supper and got them to bed without too much fuss. Then he made a cup of tea and some bread and butter for Mum, and assured her that Alfie wasn't really crying, only carrying on a bit.

He went up to the little back room at the top of the stairs to tell Fred for the last time to shut up. After all Fred was six years old. "In two years you'll be a Cub, if you behave yourself," Stan told him.

To be a Cub Scout like Stan was the height of Fred's ambition, so he did behave himself, and even Alfie was tired.

Stan tiptoed out to the back yard to say goodnight to Belle and explain why he'd had to leave her in her lonely hutch. After that there was nothing else to do but to go to bed. He used the best bedroom tonight because, after all, he was the boss. He curled up on Dad's and Mum's big bed, and although he thought he was listening for Alfie to yell, he soon went to sleep.

He woke up to hear Fred coughing. It was still pitch dark, so Stan shouted, "Shut up!" But Fred went on coughing and presently Alfie would begin to yell, and that might disturb Mum. So Stan slipped out of bed to go to the kids' room.

He opened the bedroom door, and then stood still for a moment wondering if he was still asleep and having a nightmare.

Smoke swirled up the stairs at him. Thick, grey,

STAN'S IN CHARGE

by Hazel Addis   Illustrated by Peter Harrison

4

choking smoke. He opened his mouth to shout "FIRE!" but began to cough, and then he knew that it was real, and he must do something and do it quickly.

He did. He stepped out onto the landing and shut his parents' bedroom door behind him. Then he went down on his hands and knees and crawled to the kids' room. A voice inside him seemed to say "Keep low!" and then "Get everybody *out*!" It was only later that he realised it was Akela's voice, when she had been telling them about fire-fighting. She had said that as smoke rose there was always clearer air at floor-level. The talk at Cubs had been about what to do if you found a house on fire: "Make sure everyone in the house gets out. Shut all doors and windows. Then send for the fire brigade." All this Stan remembered in a flash as he crawled to the open door of the kids' room. It was full of smoke, too, and both boys were crying and coughing.

"Fred! Alfie! UP and OUT!" Stan told them firmly, but of course they didn't move until he pulled them out of bed on to the floor.

He longed to fling open the window and scream "FIRE!" but he remembered the bit about keeping doors and windows shut. Besides, the window was twenty feet from the ground – a sheer drop – and there was no time to knot sheets and let the kids down that way . . . .

"Come *on,* Fred – downstairs, quick!" Stan was hauling Alfie, yelling of course, by the collar of his

pyjamas, and presently they were crouching at the top of the stairs, which looked like a chimney with smoke pouring up it.

"Go down, Fred!" ordered Stan.

"*Can't!* It's all smokey! *Won't* go down!"

Stan didn't have time to argue. He gave Fred a shove which started him bumping down the stairs on his bottom. Stan knew Fred might get hurt, but a few bruises were better than leaving him to roast alive or choke himself to death on the landing. Stan followed, slithering down the steep stairs with Alfie's head tucked under one arm. It hurt him and he knew it hurt Alfie with his bottom and legs bumping down the stairs behind him. But they got to the ground with a double bump.

"OUT!" panted Stan above the screams and yells of his two little brothers. Somehow he made his way to the front door, fumbled with the key in the dark, got it open and pushed both the children out into the night. There was a lovely blow of fresh, clean air and he gasped it into his choking lungs.

"Yell 'Fire'," Stan told Fred. "Loud as you can. Wake everyone up!" He saw a light go on in the house across the street and knew that Mr. Johnson would come out directly to see what all the noise was. He would look after the kids and, unlike Stan's house, Mr. Johnson's had a telephone to call the fire brigade.

Stan took a big breath of air and went back inside, slamming the door behind him.

"Shut everything!" Akela's voice rang in his ears.

neighbours came to help. Stan tumbled after, and slammed down the window.

Fred and Alfie rushed screaming to their Mum.

"Stan kicked me downstairs, Mam!" yelled Fred, scarlet with anger, but they were both able to run and shout, so they couldn't be badly hurt. Mrs. Evans from next door and Mrs. Edwards from Number 42 took the two youngsters in hand. Mrs. Johnson led Stan's Mum across the road to her house.

Mr. Johnson came over to Stan.

"Well done, lad," he said. "I've called the Fire Brigade. Shouldn't be long. You done all right, Stan."

But Stan wasn't so sure that he had done all right. He was the boss for the night and yet the house was on fire. He was a Cub who had learnt about safety in the home, and yet . . . .

As he darted up the side passage into the back yard he heard the distinctive sounds of at least one fire engine. He yanked his beautiful Belle out of her hutch and buttoned her inside his pyjama jacket. How lucky he hadn't taken her into the kitchen that night. She might have been burned alive – and now he wasn't going to have her drowned by the firemen's hoses!

When Stan's Dad got home, having been called back from the factory, the fire was out, but the firemen were still there checking over the blackened kitchen. Stan was waiting for him.

The smoke seemed thicker than ever, billowing from the open door of the kitchen. Stan went down with his nose to the floor. Half a dozen quick crawls, holding his breath, and he was able to shut the kitchen door.

Mum . . . it was extraordinary that she hadn't woken up with all the noise, but then he remembered that the Doctor had given her a sleeping pill and said she musn't be disturbed. But this was different. For a breathless moment he felt for the door knob and then he was in the front room and there was Mum sitting up in bed and looking dazed.

"Stan?" she mumbled. "I thought I heard . . ." The room was wonderfully clear of smoke and Stan shut the door quickly behind him.

"Afraid you've got to get out, Mum. There's a fire in the kitchen. The kids are out already . . ." he coughed, "in . . . the street . . ." he spluttered, " . . . wanting you."

"Fire? Oh! No!" Mum seemed to be still half asleep. "I must get some things . . ."

"You can't. You've got to get OUT!" Stan grabbed the quilt from her bed and threw it over her shoulders. His first thought was to go out through the hall. But that was full of smoke. He heaved up the sash window, and half helped, half pushed her through the window into the street. Several

"It's all right, Dad!" he shouted as he ran to his father. "We're all okay – and I'm awfully sorry about it!"

Before Stan's Dad had recovered his breath, Mr. Johnson came over. "Your Stan did all right," he said. "He got 'em all out in double-quick time, including that blessed rabbit, who's just eaten my breakfast."

Stan's Dad sighed with relief. "But what happened?" he asked. "What on earth did you do, Stan?"

"I can tell you what the boy did," said the officer in charge, who was standing close by. "He saved your wife and two young boys from a possible nasty death, and prevented your house from being burnt to the ground. As to the cause, we think it was a worn-out electric cable under the kitchen floor boards. The mice must have been nibbling it and it must have short-circuited and sparked off a fire in the mice's nest."

"The landlord said he was going to have the place re-wired last month," Stan's Dad said.

"Pity he didn't," commented the fire officer.

a table top trick

by Eric Franklin

The Disappearing Coin

All you require for this trick is an ordinary pocket handkerchief and a coin, say a 2p or a 10p piece – 50p if you are well off or can borrow it.

Spread the handkerchief as in Fig. 1 and place the coin on it a little above the centre.

Fold over the bottom point so that it overlaps the top point by 25 to 30mm or so (1 inch) – see the dotted line in Fig. 2. With both hands roll the coin and handkerchief from the base towards the points as shown in Fig. 3. Stop when the under point just pops out: the trick won't work if this point goes up and over the other point – see Fig. 4. Put a finger on the upper point (A in Fig. 4) and slowly pull the other point (B) towards you. When the handkerchief is fully out the coin will have disappeared. It is, of course, underneath the handkerchief – your magic made it pass right through. Alternatively, at that stage you can calmly pick up the handkerchief by its centre, taking up the coin at the same time, and claim to have made the coin disappear.

1

2

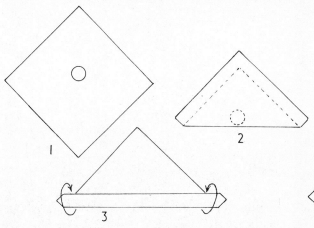

3

4

5

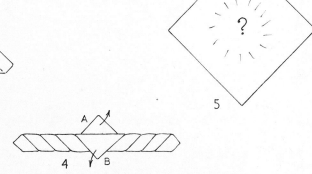

SHIP AHOY!

P. J. Stuckey LSIA tells you about some Sailing Boat Types and Rigs

1.
THE LUG SAIL is a very simple, four-sided sail, which is laced to a 'yard' along the head, and sometimes a 'boom' along the foot. The illustration shows a small dinghy with a single sail but some of the old-time fishing boats carried two or even three masts rigged with lug sails.

2.
THE SLIDING GUNTER is another four-sided sail, but the head is almost parallel to the mast, and is laced to a 'yard' which has a jaw at the lower end and slides up and down the mast. The foot is laced to a 'boom'. A small triangular sail called a jib may also be used forward of the mast, as shown.

3.
THE BERMUDAN SAIL is a tri-angular sail, the leading edge of which is usually hoisted in a track or groove in the after (rear) side of the mast.

4.
THE CATAMARAN has become very popular in recent years, although its origins are very old in the tropical oceans. It is a vessel having two identical hulls connected by a bridging deck. The illustration shows a small racing catamaran, but some are built for cruising and ocean racing and these have a cabin built across the bridging deck. With favourable wind, the catamaran is very fast.

5.
THE SLOOP RIG is illustrated in this racing dinghy. The usual crew for this type of dinghy is two, one to steer and control the mainsail, the other to control the jib.

6.
THE TRI-MARAN is a vessel with a central main hull and a smaller hull either side of it connected, like those of the catamaran, by a bridging deck. It is very fast in a favourable wind and, like the catamaran, tends to sail very upright. This tri-maran is shown using a spinnaker — a large lightweight sail used when running before the wind.

7.
THE SAILING CRUISER is a vessel having room below decks to accommodate the crew, so that they can live on board. She can be of any size or of any rig, but the majority are similar to the one shown: about 25-30 feet long, often made of glass fibre, with Terylene sails, nylon rope and frequently a metal mast and main boom. Most sailing cruisers have an auxiliary engine to help them in calms or to move about in crowded harbours. The cruiser illustrated is *sloop rigged,* having a single mast with a mainsail and one headsail which, in larger craft, is sometimes called a 'foresail' instead of a 'jib'.

8.
THE KETCH is a two-masted vessel where the forward mast is the taller of the two and is called the main mast. The after mast is called the mizzen which, in a ketch, is positioned forward of the rudder post. Another two-masted vessel, known as a YAWL, is very similar, except that the mizzen is often smaller and is positioned *behind* the rudder post. Either type may be Bermudan rigged or gaff rigged like the ketch illustrated.
The gaff sail is four-sided, with the head laced (or bent) to a spar called the gaff, while the foot is attached to the boom. Above the gaff sails may be set a topsail. The head sails consist of a stay-sail (or foresail) — so called because it is hooked (hanked) to the forward supporting wire of the mast, which is called the fore-stay and the jib, which is carried between the mast and the spar which extends beyond the bows which is called the bowsprit.

9.
THE SCHOONER is a vessel having two or more masts of equal height or where the foremast is shorter than the others. It is a fore and aft vessel — that is, the sails are set forward, behind or between the masts. However, some schooners have one or two square sails on the fore topmast. These sails are bent to spars, known as yards, which lie *across* the mast at right angles to the vessel. Such sails are called square topsails and a schooner so rigged is known as a TOPSAIL SCHOONER. The illustration shows a three-masted topsail schooner with its yards in position, but with no sails set upon them.

10.
THE GAFF CUTTER is a single-masted vessel, fore and aft, gaff rigged with gaff mainsail, topsail, staysail and jib. The mast in the cutter illustrated is made up of two parts: the lower mast and the topmast. In very bad weather the topmast may be lowered (housed) to lower the centre of gravity and thus ease the motion of the boat. The bowsprit on many cutters may also be drawn inboard when the jib is not being used. Sometimes in light winds another jib is set from the topmast head to the bowsprit, above the ordinary (working) jib. This is known as the jib topsail. The gaff cutter is an old-style vessel, but is still popular among sailors who are interested in traditional craft.

11.
THE SQUARE RIG is not seen very often in our harbours these days, except in fairly small craft. A square-rigged vessel is one in which all the principal sails are bent onto yards and set across the masts at right angles to the centreline of the vessel. These days a square-rigged vessel has at least two masts, but sometimes a mixture of square sails and fore and aft sails are used and this determines the name of the type of vessel. The word 'ship' is used to describe any large vessel nowadays, whether sail or power, but the only *real* ship is a three-masted vessel, square-rigged on all three masts. All other variations have their own names like BRIG, BRIGANTINE, BARQUE, etc. The *Cutty Sark* at Greenwich is a true ship, whereas our illustration shows a four-masted BARQUE — square rigged on three masts, and fore and aft on the fourth. It is sometimes possible to see big square-riggers when the Tall Ships Race starts from one of our own harbours.

1

2

3

4

5

6

7

8

9

10

11

What to look for in a Harbour

by Peter Stuckey

KEY

1. Tidal Harbour
2. Coastguard Look-out
3. Lighthouse
4. Ferry Slip
5. Dinghies Racing
6. Rescue Boat
7. Boats at Anchor
8. Boats on Mooring Buoys
9. Lifeboat
10. Gaff Cutter
11. Bermudan Ketch
12. Pilot Launch
13. Ship in Buoyed Channel
14. Day Mark
15. Mole
16. Fishing Boat
17. Boat Yard
18. Chandlery
19. Dinghy Park
20. Floating Harbour
21. Signal Staff
22. Lock
23. Swing Bridge
24. Commercial Wharf
25. Harbour Master's Office
26. Navigation Buoys

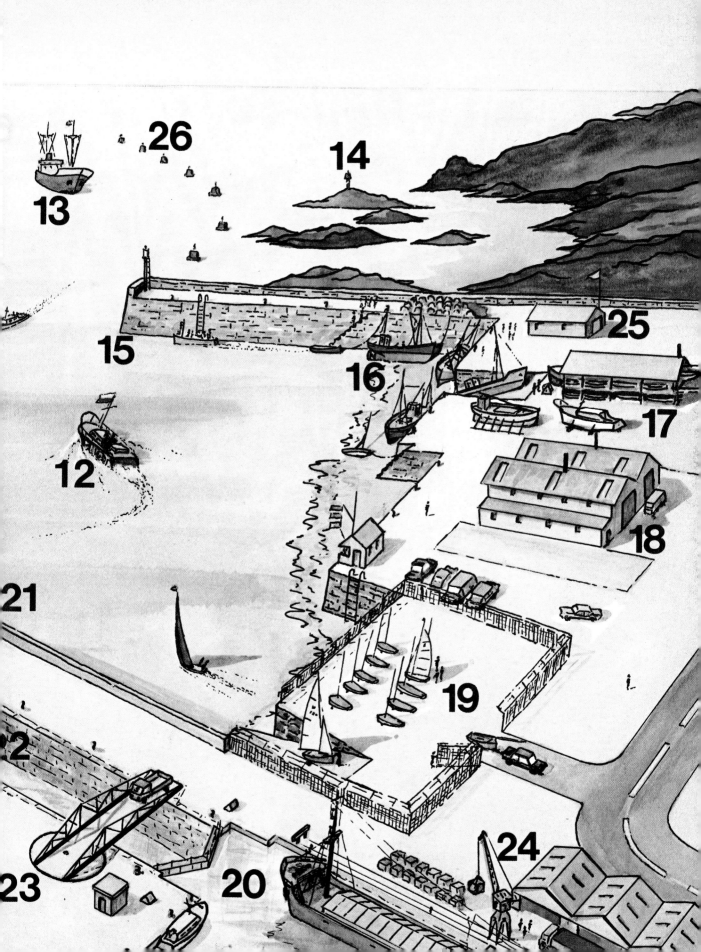

From SCENE to SCREEN

The Story of a Television Programme

Words by Martyn Day, David Harwood and Harold Wyld

Photographs by Thames Television, Laurie Curtis and Harold Wyld

Today you can bring the world into your living room at the flick of a switch. Just turn on the television and you can watch – and listen to – people, places and things from all parts of the world . . . and the moon . . . and beyond . . . . Television has become so much a part of our lives that we take it for granted. But how does a television programme get from the scene of the 'action' to the television screen in your home? The CUB SCOUT ANNUAL set out to investigate, not just any programme, but a very special one . . . one of particular interest to Cub Scouts. Here's the story of this programme from the beginning.

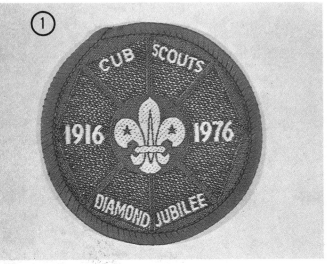

1. In 1976 Cub Scouting celebrated its 60th Birthday. It was Diamond Jubilee Year. Every Cub Scout wore this badge on his uniform.

2. During 1976 there were many items about Cub Scouting on local and national news and magazine television programmes. Here, at Thames Television's Studios at Teddington Lock near London, the idea for something more than a few seconds' 'viewing time' was born.

3. Most of you will have seen this symbol on your television screens – it's the one which introduces Thames Television's popular children's programme 'Magpie', which is 'networked' to all Independent Television Companies.

4. Martyn Day, who is one of Magpie's Researchers, is always on the lookout for material to include in the programme. The January 1976 edition of *Scouting*, The Scout Association's monthly magazine, had a special mention of 60 Years of Cub Scouting. That set Martyn (who was a Scout) thinking about a programme on Cub Scouts . . . but what sort of programme should it be?

5. A telephone call to Jack Olden (The Scout Association's Public Relations Officer) in March was the starting point for meetings and discussions between the Magpie team and the Scouts to find out what might be possible.

6. Early in June, Lesley Burgess (Magpie's Producer) and Martyn, having gathered a lot of information about possibilities, meet at a programme planning session. They decide that a whole programme will be devoted to Cub Scouts, with one of the Cub Adventure Days at Gilwell in August providing a possible location.

7. Lesley Burgess 'chalks up' the special Cub Scout programme on her forward planning board. Although there are several weeks to go before the programme is made, there are a host of things to be done. As the programme will be recorded on location, the outside broadcast unit has to be booked. Gilwell will have to be visited by both the technical and production teams to decide where cameras will be placed, what activity will be happening where, and so on.

9. . . . Bill Boot, the Senior Graphics Technician, then mounts the photographs . . .

8. The programme will be recorded on Wednesday 4th August, and will be transmitted on Tuesday 10th August. In July Gilwell is visited by the Magpie team and a preliminary 'shooting schedule' is drawn up. Back at the studios, work goes on on other material to be included. For example, here's Graphics Designer Mick Manville (sitting) and Martyn Day sorting through and selecting the historical photographs (supplied by the Public Relations Department of Scout Headquarters) to be used . . .

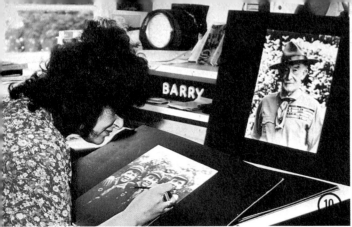

10. . . . and finally Graphics Designer Ruth Bribram re-touches the photographs ready for the camera.

11. At 7.00 a.m. on Wednesday 4th August, after almost nine months' preparation and planning, the outside broadcast unit (which is shown here on another location in London), the presenters and the production team leave Teddington for Epping Forest and Gilwell. "We needed the early start to ensure that all our gear was set up by the time the thousands of Cubs arrived," Martyn remembers. It's going to be a long, hot day!

RUNNING ORDER RECORDING OUT OF ORDER	- a -	MAGPIE - CUBS	

ITEM		LOCATION	APPROX RT
1	Hello & Welcome MICK/DOUG	1 - The Quick	0.30
2	History of Cubs JENNY	2 - Buffalo Lawn	3.30
3	Hot Air Balloon MICK	3 - Training Ground	3.30
4	God's Eye Craft DOUG	AB	3.30
5	Sausage Sizzle JENNY/DOUG/MICK	4 - Bomb Hole	3.30
6	Assault Course MICK/JENNY	AB	4.00
7	Hovercraft DOUG	3 - Training Ground	3.40
8	Grand Howl JENNY/MICK/DOUG	1 - The Quick	1.30
9	End credits Cubs + roller	AB	0.30

12. A copy of a page of the 'script' which shows the 'running order' of the programme and how long each part will last.

13. Once at Gilwell the equipment is set up and tested, while the presenters and others who will appear in the programme get ready to face the cameras. This photograph shows the interior of the truck which contains all the equipment, which is commonly called the scanner. The pictures and sound from each camera position can be seen and heard on these television monitors, and recorded on videotape recording machines. These machines work in much the same way as tape recorders except that the $\frac{1}{2}$-inch tape records colour pictures as well as sound. The people in this picture (from left to right) are Unit Supervisor Phil Haines, Vision Mixer John Cooper and Production Assistant Maggi Hilliard.

14. On the Buffalo Lawn, behind the main house, the programme will be introduced by Jenny Hanley, wearing a 1916 Cub Mistress's uniform (which was, incidentally, supplied by Thames Television's Wardrobe Department after a lot of research). There are also Cub Scouts in uniforms from the early days to the present day and there's to be an interview with Hazel Addis, who was one of the first 'Lady Cubmasters' in 1915 and who has retained an active interest in Scouting ever since (not least in writing books, stories and articles for and about Cub Scouts – you don't have to look further than the pages of this Annual for evidence of this!)

Photograph 11 and Script 12 by courtesy of Thames Television

(15)

15. Checking the sound level for part of Jenny's introduction. The person in the front is David Dowling, the Floor Manager. He is listening to instructions from Joe Boyer (the Director) on his earphones, which the technicians call 'cans'.

16. The final details of Hazel Addis's interview are checked before recording. The very large music stand on the left is a caption stand. It carries all the captions, including historical photographs, Titles and End Credits, all of which are mounted on large cards. "By the way," adds Martyn Day, "we do not use a prompter on Magpie. Each presenter has a 'fact sheet' beforehand and then they create their own dialogue as they go along . . . a skilled task!"

For the next few hours, the Magpie team moves about Gilwell from one location to another recording the activities of Cub Adventure Day and a number of the 'special attractions' which show some of the things a Cub Scout can look forward to when he becomes a Scout and a Venture Scout.

(16)

17. A team from the Scout's National Air Activities Centre at Lasham in Hampshire put up their Thunder AX 7 hot air balloon with Magpie's Mick Robertson and Lasham's aviator Terry Jones in the basket. Both wear miniature radio microphones so their 'chat' can be recorded on the ground . . . .

(17)

(18)

18. Douglas Rae went for a run (or should it be drive or flight?) in Lasham's two-seater Hoverservices Scarab 3 sporting and racing hovercraft with its two Choler engines – the craft can reach speeds of more than 60 mph . . . .

19. Mick (in the red protective suit) had a go over the obstacle course in and around the Bomb Hole.

(19)

20. There was a chance to 'have a go' at activities like God's Eye craft and making pasta pictures . . . .

21. One 'stand' which attracted the crowds as well as the cameras was *Scouting* magazine's Super Sausage Sizzling Spectacular – the brainchild of Norman Garnett, Sub-Editor of *Scouting's* Cub Scout Supplement – which was a lighthearted nationwide competition, run during Jubilee year, which challenged Packs all over the country to cook the longest sausage. The rules of the competition stated that the cooking had to be done outdoors, the sausage had to be measured in metres and centimetres, and the cooked sausage had to retain a modicum of respectability, be properly cooked and, as far as possible, still be in one piece. Over 500 Packs entered. The winners were the 69th Sheffield with 440 metres 10 centimetres, with the 2nd Hertford (350 metres) runners-up, and the 11th Sheffield (326 metres 20 cms) third. The 2nd Hertford Cub Scouts repeated their performance by cooking a 305 metre sausage over a giant foil frying-pan in front of the television cameras, and Magpie presenter Jenny chatted to Ron Jeffries (the General Editor of The Scout Association) and the 2nd Hertford boys.

23. . . . huge Grand Howl, led by Jenny, followed by the singing of Kumbaya.

It was 5.00 p.m. The recording was complete. The crew de-rigged the equipment before returning to base. With them, the Magpie team had all the ingredients for the programme 'on tape'. There would now be a lot of editing work to put all the pieces together to make a well-balanced 24-minute programme for transmission.

22. As the afternoon drew to a close, and the evening shadows lengthened, the Unit and hundreds of Cub Scouts moved to The Quick for the finale. This was to be a . . .

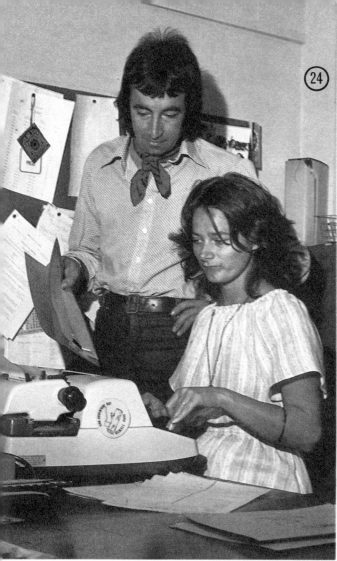

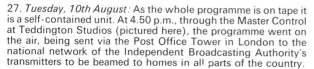

24. *Monday, 9th August:* Martyn and Production Assistant Maggi Hilliard check the final script.

27. *Tuesday, 10th August:* As the whole programme is on tape it is a self-contained unit. At 4.50 p.m., through the Master Control at Teddington Studios (pictured here), the programme went on the air, being sent via the Post Office Tower in London to the national network of the Independent Broadcasting Authority's transmitters to be beamed to homes in all parts of the country.

25. Editing the videotape recording (known as a VTR). Editor Fred Turner (left) with 'Magpie' Director Joe Boyer (right) and Production Assistant Maggi Hilliard look at what has been recorded and note which sections they wish to select.

26. The programme is nearing completion. Engineer Bernard Hill runs part of the VTR at Gilwell, while in an adjoining part of the editing suite Fred Turner re-records the required sections for the final programme. Before they go home tonight, the complete tape must be ready for transmission . . . .

Photograph 27 by courtesy of Thames Television

What do you know about the COUNTRYSIDE COMMISSION?

1.

The Countryside Commission encourages people to care for and to look after the natural beauty of the scenery in England and Wales. It also encourages and helps to provide facilities for people to get into the countryside and to enjoy themselves informally.

2.

The Commission is not an organisation that individual people can join. It is an independent public agency which was set up by Parliament in 1968 to help protect our national landscape heritage. It uses Government money to provide grants for country parks, picnic sites, tree-planting, information centres, footpath improvements and other conservation and recreation work. It also looks into major countryside issues; its work on studying the conservation of our coastline led to the creation of the new heritage coasts, the first of which can be seen on the map.

 Look out for this sign – the symbol which shows a country park has been recognised by the Countryside Commission.

3.

The Commission is also responsible for designating national parks and areas of outstanding natural beauty as well as long-distance footpaths and bridleways, all of which are shown on the map. There's a special photofeature on 'Your National Parks' on the next page.

 This acorn symbol shows a long-distance footpath or bridleway which has been designated by the Countryside Commission.

Map

NATIONAL PARKS

AREAS OF OUTSTANDING
NATURAL BEAUTY

LONG-DISTANCE FOOTPATHS
AND BRIDLEWAYS

DEFINED HERITAGE COASTS

North
Northumberland

Northumberland
Coast

Tyne
and
Wear

Cleveland
Way

North Yorkshire

NORTH YORK
MOORS

YORKSHIRE
DALES

Pennine
Way

West
Yorkshire

South
Yorkshire

Lincolnshire
Wolds

PEAK
DISTRICT

Cannock
Chase

West
Midlands

North Norfolk
completely defined

Norfolk
Coast

Suffolk Coast
and Heaths

Suffolk

Cotswolds

Dedham Vale

The
Ridgeway
Path

Chilterns

Greater
London

North
Downs Way

Surrey
Hills

Kent
Downs

North
Wessex
Downs

East
Hampshire

Sussex Downs

South
Downs Way

North
Hampshire
Coast

Hamstead

Chichester
Harbour

Sussex
completely defined

Tennyson

Isle of Wight

Based on the Ordnance Survey map
© Crown copyright 1976

10   0   70   kms
10   0   50 miles

4.
The Commission also sponsors research and experiments. These are mainly practical and are designed to find ways of dealing with some of the problems of our using land in the countryside for so many conflicting purposes. For instance, the Commission pioneered farm 'open days' in England and Wales to help bring farmers and countryside visitors closer together. It has run cycle hire schemes to help people who do not have their own private car or other transport and also to persuade more people to get out of their cars, which tend to block up the countryside and create eyesores when they are parked in major beauty spots.

5.
The Commission also encourages people to learn about and to follow the Country Code (turn to page 56 for a special feature on the Country Code). By following the ten simple slogans which the Code contains, every person can make his or her own contribution to conserving the beauty of the countryside, making sure that it is there for us all to enjoy for a long time to come.

6.
The Commission produces leaflets and other publications to do with the Country Code, the national parks, country parks, and many other countryside matters. These are available through Cub Scout Leaders from the Commission Headquarters at John Dower House, Crescent Place, Cheltenham, Glos, GL50 3RA.

19

The photograph shows Snowdon

Your National Parks

1. SNOWDONIA: A wild, mountainous region crossed by high passes, which offers some of the best rock-climbing and mountain walking for both the beginner and the expert. You'll find fine woodlands too, as well as Nature Reserves and grand coastal landscapes.

The photograph shows Derwentwater and Saddleback.

2. LAKE DISTRICT: Spectacular mountain scenery with wooded lower slopes and beautiful lakes and tarns are a feature of the Park. Here there are England's highest mountains – Scafell Pike, Helvellyn and Skiddaw – and nearly all her biggest lakes, including Windermere, which is the largest.

The photograph shows ponies at Hay Bluff

3. PEMBROKESHIRE COAST: A breathtaking section of the Welsh coastline where impressive cliffs alternate with secluded bays and sandy coves. In the rolling uplands to the north are lots of pre-historic relics. There's also a chain of Norman Castles and St. David's Cathedral.

The photograph shows the craggy rocks at St. Govan

4. BRECON BEACONS: Centred on 'The Beacons', the Park stretches from the Black Mountains in the east to Dyfed's Black Mountain to the west. Vast stretches of open common land are flanked by softer, pastoral country. The limestone area contains Britain's longest known cave system.

5. EXMOOR: The scenery is very varied. There's the magnificent coastline behind which is a heather-clad moorland plateau seamed with finely wooded combes. In the east are the Brendon Hills with their patchwork of stone farmsteads and large fields. Red deer and ponies roam wild on the moor.

The photograph shows Dunster in Somerset

The photograph shows part of Hadrian's Wall near Housesteads

6. NORTHUMBERLAND: A region of hills and moorland, adjoining the Border Forest Park and stretching from Hadrian's Roman Wall in the south to the Cheviot Hills on the Scottish Border. This is Border country, rich in historical interest, with wide views over a remote and varied countryside of hill and valley, heather moor and grass-clad fell.

8. YORKSHIRE DALES: An area of wide, sweeping upland moors, cut by deep pastoral valleys. Here you'll find some of the finest limestone scenery in Britain as well as part of the Pennine Way. Bridges, barns and houses are nearly all built of stone.

9. DARTMOOR: This is the largest area of high moorland in southern England, famous for its granite 'tors' which are often weathered into fantastic shapes. Much of the moor is heather-clad, but it has many boggy places, rich in plant life. There are delightful villages, churches, farmhouses and bridges.

The photograph shows part of the moor from Hound Tor

The photograph shows Malham Cove, Yorkshire

7. NORTH YORK MOORS: The Park stretches from the Hambledon Hills in the west to the sandy bays and high rugged headlands above Scarborough. There's solitary grandeur in the heart of the moor which is intersected by beautiful wooded valleys and covered with bracken and purple heather.

The photograph shows Pen-y-Ghent

10. PEAK DISTRICT: In the south and east are limestone uplands; finely wooded dales with swift, clear rivers, and unspoilt villages. To the north are wild moorlands edged by gritstone crags. Sports for the adventurous include climbing, caving, gliding and, in winter, skiing.

The photograph shows Froggart Edge.

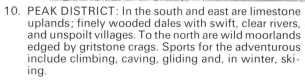

22

Wildlife in a Town

by Peter Harrison

If you live in a town you may think that there's not much wildlife about. But look around! You will not have to look far. The picture shows you just a few of the many animals, plants and birds which you can discover in a built-up area.

1.
ROSE BAY WILLOW HERB is often called 'Fireweed' because it grows well in ground which has been burnt by fire.

2.
THE HOUSE MOUSE usually lives in houses, eating scraps which we humans leave lying about. It is very adaptable and will often make a home in a wall in the summer months.

3.
PEACOCK 4. RED ADMIRAL 5. SMALL TORTOISESHELL: These butterflies are all members of the Vanessid family which has some of Britain's biggest and most beautiful butterflies. They will often migrate to the warmer climates of Southern Europe or North Africa for the winter.

6.
BUDDLEIA: In mid-summer this plant's scented lilac flowers attract all kinds of insects, particularly the butterflies we have shown. It grows quickly and spreads over derelict ground.

7.
GROUNDSEL is a short-lived weed which thrives on open ground. It is very adaptable and will grow in almost any soil and in all weather conditions. It flowers and seeds throughout the year. Goldfinches like its fluffy seeds which are also often fed to caged birds — hence its nickname 'Birdseed'.

8.
BRAMBLES are rough prickly shrubs, particularly wild blackberries. Butterflies feed from the fruit when it is very ripe and mushy.

9.
THE BANDED SNAIL hibernates until mid-summer and then comes out in damp weather.

10.
THE SHIELD BUG will often be found on brambles. The female of the species hides her young on the underside of a bramble leaf and then keeps guard on the upper surface to keep away her enemies.

11.
THE HEDGEHOG stays hidden during the day and comes out at night to hunt for food. It has a very keen sense of smell. It protects itself by rolling into a ball, thus erecting its sharp spines.

12.
SWIFTS spend more time in the air than any other birds. Their legs have become very weak because they use them so little. They migrate to Africa, south of the Equator, for the winter.

CUB SCOUTS IN ACTION
Learning by Doing

COOKING – not all Cub Scout cooking is done over smokey – or even non-smokey! – fires as these lads from Dorset demonstrate as they busily prepare pancakes over gas stoves.

ART – "Just let me have a brush, a piece of paper and a little paint, and I'll create a genuine original painting for you." Cub Scouting gives boys great opportunities to be creative.

TRACKING – "Yes, I'm sure that's where we're meant to go!" Cub Scouts from Lincoln follow tracking signs to . . . who knows where? *They'll* know when they get to the end of the trail!

TRAVELLING – Cub Scouts travel in many ways – but perhaps not very often in a home-made hovercraft like this one built at the National Scout Air Activities Centre at Lasham in Hampshire.

Photographs by Laurie Curtis

be your own CALCULATOR

How often have you wanted to measure something but haven't got a measure or a ruler? You can get a reasonable idea simply by using *yourself*. However, you will need to have some details about yourself before you can be your own calculator.

Distances

To measure distances you must know the length of your stride. Here's how to work it out. Mark out a straight line exactly 25 metres long. Walk up and down the line four times. Count the number of steps you take each time from one end of the line to the other. Divide the total distance covered (4 × 25 metres = 100 metres) by the *total* number of steps you *take* and the answer will be the length of your average stride. Fill in YOUR details here *in pencil*.

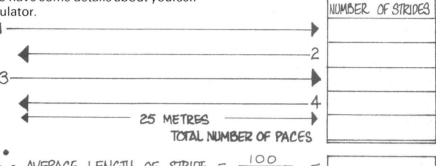

NUMBER OF STRIDES

1

2

3

4

25 METRES
TOTAL NUMBER OF PACES

AVERAGE LENGTH OF STRIDE = $\dfrac{100}{}$ =

Other measurements

Fill in the blanks on this diagram *in pencil*. You will probably need to ask Mum or Dad or a friend to help you with some of them. You'll then be able to estimate the sizes of all sorts of things. We've suggested you use pencil, so that you can check yourself every few months and make any changes as you grow older.

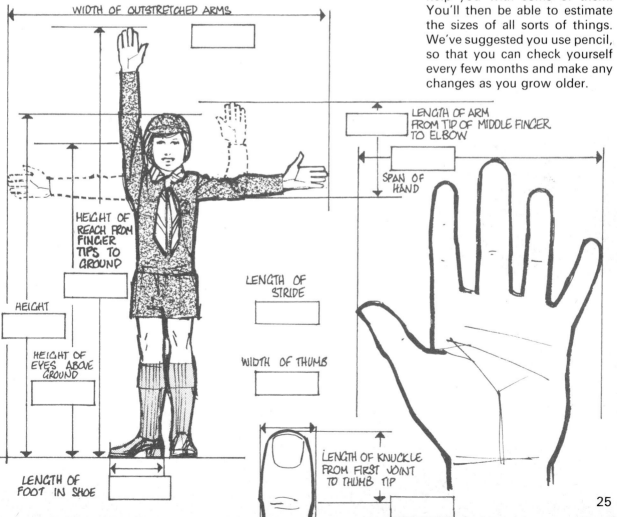

WIDTH OF OUTSTRETCHED ARMS

HEIGHT OF REACH FROM FINGER TIPS TO GROUND

HEIGHT

HEIGHT OF EYES ABOVE GROUND

LENGTH OF FOOT IN SHOE

LENGTH OF STRIDE

WIDTH OF THUMB

LENGTH OF ARM FROM TIP OF MIDDLE FINGER TO ELBOW

SPAN OF HAND

LENGTH OF KNUCKLE FROM FIRST JOINT TO THUMB TIP

Making an Impression

Some information about Brass Rubbing
by
LEIGH CHAPMAN
Director, Brass Rubbing Centres

Illustrations copyright © Brass Rubbing Centres Ltd.

Brass Rubbing sounds a very strange thing to do, but more and more it is becoming a popular hobby. Perhaps you have seen people doing brass rubbings on the floors of churches. They may be on their knees, but they are not praying! They are methodically rubbing wax over the surface of a piece of paper until the design of the brass underneath – which may be a knight in armour – shows through!

The brasses set into the floors of some of our old churches are often more than 500 years old. They can be worn and damaged, but usually you can see the details of costume and armour as it used to be worn by our forefathers. If you feel the surface of a brass in a church with your fingers you will find it cold to the touch. The design is cut into the surface, the lines being grooves which were made by the Mediaeval craftsman, using a tool like a pointed chisel.

Brasses were originally made as memorials to people and their designs show us how these people appeared. There are brasses showing knights and ladies, bishops, merchants, priests, schoolmasters, and even lawyers. Through studying brasses much has been learned about the development of armour and weapons and also about changes in men's and women's fashions.

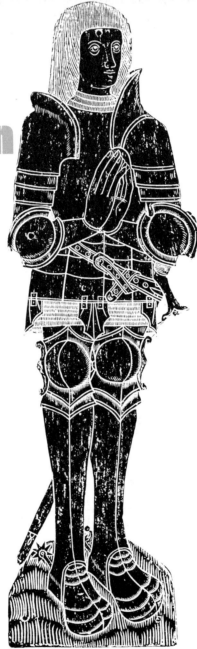

JOHN HAREWELL 1505

THOMAS CHAUCER 1436

The oldest brasses in England are more than 700 years old. They are over six feet long and show men clad in chain mail and carrying heavy swords and shields. Soon the use of plate armour developed and by studying brasses we can see how it changed over the centuries. The men clad in armour were usually local land-owners, but sometimes they were famous knights who fought for their country at battles such as the Battle of Agincourt; others held high office at the Royal Court.

A typical complete brass memorial consists of the full length figures of the man and his wife, an inscription in Latin saying who he was, small brasses showing his sons and daughters and perhaps a decorative canopy and a heraldic shield. Brasses to merchants usually incorporated the merchant's mark by which mediaeval merchants were recognised.

There are other more unusual brasses, probably the ones which seem strangest to us now

JOHN CROSTON AND WIFE 1470

Sir ANTHONY FETYPLACE 1510

are the so-called 'gruesome' or 'shroud' brasses. They show emaciated skeletons wrapped up in a shroud. An example in Oxfordshire even shows the body being devoured by worms!

If you want to make your own collection of brass rubbings, ask for a book at the public library which has a list of the churches with brasses. It is very important to *write* to the vicar of the church and obtain permission before you do a brass rubbing.

The other way to make your own rubbings is to visit a Brass Rubbing Centre. These are exhibitions of exact replica memorial brasses where visitors are supplied with materials and any instruction they may need. Brass Rubbing Centres are organised by cathedrals, museums and similar organisations. If you have difficulty in finding your nearest Brass Rubbing Centre or want to know where to buy materials, write for information to Brass Rubbing Centres Ltd., 48a Ashcroft Road, Cirencester, Glos., enclosing a stamped addressed envelope.

27

The Chief Scout, Sir William Gladstone Bt DL MA leads a very full life. He enjoys travelling to meet Members of the Movement whenever he can. As Chief Scout he has a very full diary. Here ED LUCAS give you a glimpse of a weekend in the life of the Chief when, in the summer of 1976, he accompanied Sir William on a tour of seven Scottish Counties, making it a . . .

Sir William Gladstone, Chief Scout, boards a Piper Aztec in Edinburgh to fly 120 miles north to Moray.

FLYING VISIT TO SCOTLAND

They drove the Chief Scout and the Chief Commissioner for Scotland the fourteen miles over rough country into the Lammermuir Hills. They arrived at an empty field. They hoped the Scouts would arrive. And they did!

With rucksacks on backs, they came from all parts of East Lothian, ready to set up their hike camp. This was the start of the Chief Scout's Scottish Tour, on a warm June Friday afternoon.

On Saturday the Chief Scout was in the West of Scotland, visiting boys from Renfrew and Inverclyde in camp. In the afternoon he flew by a Royal Navy Sea-King helicopter to Edinburgh, where 2,000 Cubs and Scouts were enjoying a programme with an international theme.

That evening the Chief watched water activities in the shadow of the Forth Bridges before a final camp fire at the Bonaly Camping and Training Centre.

At 8.30 on Sunday Sir William boarded a Piper Aztec at Edinburgh Airport, flying 120 miles north to Moray to see Cub Scout Highland Games and Venture Scout activities. A quick dash by car and the Chief Scout was in camp at Inverness, meeting boys from a very wide area of the Scottish Highlands. Next a radio interview, a rushed meal, then back into the aircraft to fly a further 80 miles north to be in readiness for the visit to Caithness.

The journey on Monday morning was by Vintage Rolls Royce to see the Cub Scout Olympics, the Scouts in camp and for a discussion with Venture Scouts and Ranger Guides. Later the Chief flew over the Pentland Firth to Orkney to meet the only Scout Group on the Islands. The Chief's last engagement was at the Investiture of four new Orcadian Scouts.

The sun was setting over Scapa Flow as the Chief's aircraft flew south at the end of a happy flying visit to some of Scotland's Scouts.

The Chief Scout meets the Bowmen of Inverness

28

Right at the start of the tour the Chief met Scouts from all parts of East Lothian at their hike camp site in the Lammermuir Hills.

The Chief meets Cub Scouts in Orkney during his whirlwind tour of Scotland and finds time to talk with boys and leaders.

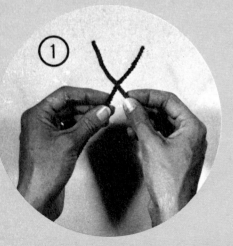

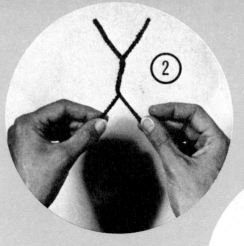

1. Place one cleaner over another.
2. Twist them round each other two or three times to make the body.
3. Join the top to make the head.

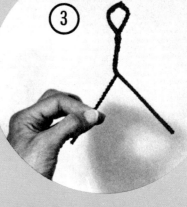

PIPE CLEANER FIGURES

Fun to make . . . quick to make . . .

What you will need: packets of pipe cleaners. Coloured pipe cleaners are more expensive than white ones, but they can be worth the extra money to make a good pipe cleaner figure into a great one. On this page you can see how to make a person. When you've got the idea, you can make up figures of your own. Take care of your cleaners and you'll be able to use them again and again.

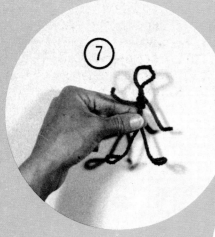

4. Bend the bottom of the legs to form the feet.
5. Put a third pipe cleaner across the top of the body.
6. Twist round body twice . . . now the figure has arms.
7. Bend the arms for elbows and hands . . . and the figure is complete.

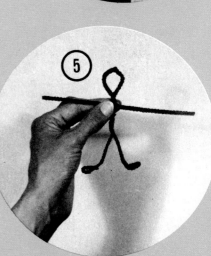

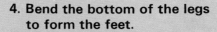

BANANA BOATS

IF YOU HAVE A BANANA ON YOUR NEXT PACK OUTING PICNIC, DON'T PEEL OFF THE SKIN COMPLETELY; INSTEAD TAKE ONE SECTION OFF ONLY

by Nancy Scott   Illustrated by Peter Harrison

NOW SCOOP OUT THE BANANA WITH A KNIFE OR SPOON

YOU CAN TURN THE PEEL INTO A BOAT BY INSERTING TWO SMALL TWIGS — THESE ARE ALSO THE SEATS.

IF YOUR BOAT SHOULD PROVE TOO LIGHT ON THE WATER, THEN WEIGHT IT DOWN WITH A FEW SMALL PEBBLES.

WITH THESE BOATS YOU CAN HAVE GREAT FUN ON ANY WATER.

BUT I'M SURE YOUR IMAGINATION NEEDS NO FURTHER SUGGESTIONS AS TO WHAT YOU CAN DO WITH THEM.

a table top trick

Coin Circle
by Eric Franklin

For this trick, you need six coins, say 2p pieces. Lay them down on the table exactly as in FIG. 1. The trick is to move only three coins, one at a time, so that the six form a circle. First, invite your friends to try – then do it for them. Then arrange the coins again. To their surprise, it won't work for them although you have just done it in front of them.

Here are the moves – and the secret. First, move coin D so that it touches E and F. (Figs. 1 and 2). Next, move E so that it touches A and B (Figs. 2 and 3). Lastly, move A so that it touches E and D (Fig 3) and your circle is made. To fool your friends, then arrange the coins as in Fig 4. They will try and copy your moves and won't succeed. *You* can then do it, by starting with F and working from right to left.

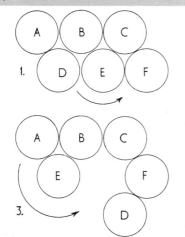

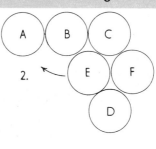

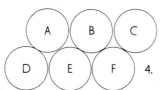

John Sweet invites you to try

the great pyramid CROSSWORD

Illustrated by Jane Phipps

Climb up and down the great pyramid by filling in the empty squares with words or phrases beginning with the appropriate letters. Note that all the squares must be filled. Here are the clues:–

A. A very small insect.
B. Can be very painful.
C. A Jester.
D. To protect.
E. To approve or agree.
F. To predict.
G. Salutations.
H. Level.
I. Tummy upset.
J. Upstart.
K. Taunt on Calvary.
L. Screenplay about a party of boys marooned on a desert island.
M. Keep away from these cats.

N. "Be it ever so humble, there's —"
O. Athletes do it in their stride.
P. Heir-apparent to the throne of England.
Q. A black Queen. Quite a card!
R. Acknowledgement.
S. Scouting skills.
T. A large tract of land.
U. Precarious.
V. Old timer.
W. A scarf ring or slide.
X. A three-masted Mediterranean ship.
Y. A citizen of the U.S.A.
Z. Collection of wild creatures in captivity.

Solution on page 62.

Make a Waterscope for Underwater Observation

In ponds and pools and gently flowing streams, a Waterscope enables you to observe underwater animal and plant life without wetting your feet, and without surface ripples and reflections disturbing clear vision. Here's how you can make your own Waterscope:

1. Cut a 60 cm (24 inch) length of piping such as 8cm (3¼ inch) diameter plastic down-piping as used with roof guttering. (Other plastic or metal piping with a diameter of 8cm to about 10cm – 3¼ inch to 4 inch – can also be used). From a hobby shop, get a piece of transparent plastic (plexiglass) about 2mm (¹/₁₆ inch) thick, and cut out a circle to the inner diameter of your pipe. This is for your underwater 'window' at one end of the pipe.

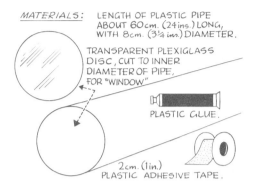

MATERIALS: LENGTH OF PLASTIC PIPE ABOUT 60cm. (24ins.) LONG, WITH 8cm. (3¼ in.) DIAMETER.

TRANSPARENT PLEXIGLASS DISC, CUT TO INNER DIAMETER OF PIPE, FOR "WINDOW"

PLASTIC GLUE.

2cm. (1in.) PLASTIC ADHESIVE TAPE.

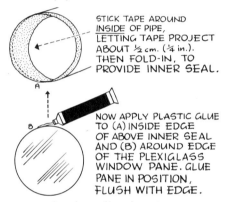

STICK TAPE AROUND INSIDE OF PIPE, LETTING TAPE PROJECT ABOUT ½ cm. (¼ in.). THEN FOLD-IN, TO PROVIDE INNER SEAL.

NOW APPLY PLASTIC GLUE TO (A) INSIDE EDGE OF ABOVE INNER SEAL AND (B) AROUND EDGE OF THE PLEXIGLASS WINDOW PANE. GLUE PANE IN POSITION, FLUSH WITH EDGE.

2. With 2cm (1 inch) wide plastic tape, line the inside of the 'window' end of the pipe but let about ½cm (¼ inch) of tape protrude. This, when folded back inside will provide an inner seal. Apply a suitable plastic adhesive (glue) to the inside edge of the above inner seal, and also all round the edge of your plexiglass 'window' and glue the window pane in position.

3 Now run plastic adhesive tape around the outside of the pipe, at the window end – allowing the tape to extend about ½cm (¼ inch) beyond the end of the pipe. Then gently but firmly press this tape extension over the outer edge of the window, to make a tight seal. (Be sure the glue holding the window in position is dry before you do this). At the other end of the pipe – the viewing end – cushion the pipe around the circumference with plastic adhesive tape – to provide a soft surface when you use the Waterscope.

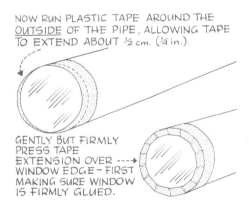

NOW RUN PLASTIC TAPE AROUND THE OUTSIDE OF THE PIPE, ALLOWING TAPE TO EXTEND ABOUT ½ cm. (¼ in.).

GENTLY BUT FIRMLY PRESS TAPE EXTENSION OVER WINDOW EDGE – FIRST MAKING SURE WINDOW IS FIRMLY GLUED.

CUT AND FILE VIEWING END TO FIT AROUND YOUR NOSE. TAPE EDGES.

4. To use your Waterscope, kneel down at the water's edge, with the window end under water and close to the aquatic life you wish to observe. With the above 8cm diameter pipe, put the Waterscope to one eye, in telescope fashion. However, if you use one of larger diameter – say 10cm or a little more – you can use both eyes.

Used with permission of the World Scout Bureau/World Wildlife Fund.

Legend of Kenfig Pool

by Geoffrey D. Hemming

Illustrated by Annabel Spenceley

I EXPECT you've heard of the legendary monster that's reputed to lurk in the murky depths of Scotland's famous Loch Ness. But did you know that there are lakes in other parts of the British Isles with great tales of mystery attached to them?

One such lake lies in mid-Glamorgan, South Wales, and is called Kenfig Pool. On the site now dominated by water once stood a magnificent city.

The city was very prosperous and travellers came from all parts to buy and sell their wares. It even had its own castle with a garrison of soldiers to protect it from invaders. Around the city stood high walls and at night the great doors were bolted so no one could enter or leave.

One stormy night a weary traveller arrived at Kenfig and begged for shelter within the city walls. The guards at the gate merely laughed at him and with their abuse ringing in his ears, he was ordered away.

The traveller, who was a man of nobility and with a purse heavy with gold, turned and disappeared into the darkness. He was never seen alive again. In the cold dawn his battered body was discovered and his gold had gone.

Outside the city walls lived a very poor farmer who had just proposed an offer of marriage to the daughter of one of Kenfig's noblemen. The nobleman laughed at the farmer. "When your gold matches mine my daughter shall be your bride," he informed him.

Dressed in clothes of exquisite silk, the farmer returned to the nobleman and again requested to marry his daughter. At the sight of the farmer's gold the nobleman gave his permission and at once ordered the wedding banquet to be prepared. He didn't stop to ask the farmer from where he had obtained his sudden wealth.

On the day of the wedding as the guests sang and danced and downed their ale, a ghostly voice was heard to cry out: *"May my curse be upon your children's children!"* The threat was repeated. Then complete silence fell over the banqueting hall.

Terrified, the guests fled to their homes leaving behind a very frightened farmer and a puzzled nobleman and his daughter.

Several years passed and the farmer and his wife were blessed with three fine sons. Eventually the boys grew up and one day the eldest son announced that he had met a very beautiful girl whom he wished to marry.

After his marriage the son took his bride and went to live abroad and only returned to Kenfig after the birth of their baby boy. The farmer, now one of the city's wealthiest men, was so delighted to have a grandson that he threw a great celebration feast and invited the whole of Kenfig's population to attend.

As the merriment reached its peak the same ghostly voice they had heard many years before, rang out once more. *"My curse is upon you. My curse has come."*

A sudden wind screamed through the city streets and rain lashed down against its walls. Great cracks

appeared across the floor of the banqueting hall and as they parted water gushed up and flooded the building.

The storm lasted for many days and when it ceased those who dared to venture near from neighbouring towns discovered a large pool where once the city had stood. All that remained of Kenfig was the large bell tower that had stood in the centre. The top of the tower and its bell were just visible above the water. But in time the water rose even higher and the bell slipped out of sight.

Today Kenfig Pool is very popular with bathers and many have claimed that on a clear day they have seen the ruined houses far below in their watery grave. It is also said that when the wind blows in from the sea and the tide is at its highest, the old city bell can be heard under the water ringing out its tale of woe.

If ever you visit the pool, stand quietly for a while and listen – maybe the wind will be in the right direction and you'll hear the bell for yourself.

Robert Baden-Powell was the man whose ideas, imagination and inspiration gave Scouting and Guiding to the young people of the world. First as a famous soldier and then as Founder of the Scout and Girl Guide Movements, he travelled to many corners of the earth. If you do some research, you may well find some 'evidence' of B.-P. staying at, or visiting, a place near your home. Many of you either live in London or will visit it one day. In this feature you can see, and read a little about, just a few of the places in London which have connections with the Founder. So come with Cub Scouts Michael Kavanagh and David Anderson of Squirrels Heath, and Carola Kaye (The Scout Association's Director of Cub Scout Training) . . .

In the Footsteps of B.-P.

You'll find this bronze replica of Baden-Powell's footstep at Gilwell Park. It was given to Gilwell by the Scouts of Hungary.

This fine bust of B.-P. is also at Gilwell, presented by the Mexican Scout Association.

1.

CHARTERHOUSE, Charterhouse Square, EC1: In 1870, B.-P. went to Charterhouse School as a Gownboy Foundationer. He was then 13 years old. He spent his first two years in these buildings close to the famous Smithfield meat markets before the school moved to Godalming in Surrey. The buildings are now occupied by the Charterhouse Sutton's Hospital.

2.

THE BEEFSTEAK CLUB, Irving Street, WC2: B.-P. was a member of a number of clubs in London, including this one. It has a most unusual door which is probably much the same as it was when B.-P. went there . . . of course, the shops would have been *very* different!

3.
WESTMINSTER ABBEY: Although B.-P. died, and was buried, in Africa, there is a memorial tablet to him on the floor of the Chapel of St. George in Westminster Abbey. It was unveiled on Wednesday, April 23rd 1947, St. George's Day. As you can see from this replica of the tablet – which is in Baden-Powell House – the inscription has the Scout Badge on one side and the Girl Guides' Badge on the other.

4.
25 BUCKINGHAM PALACE ROAD, SW1: B.-P.'s first Scout 'headquarters' was a little office in Henrietta Street near Charterhouse. It became too small, so it moved to larger premises in Victoria Street in 1909. So great was the growth of the Movement that in 1917 'Imperial Headquarters' moved to 25 Buckingham Palace Road where it remained until 1974. Today the ground floor is still the main London shop of Scout Shops Ltd.

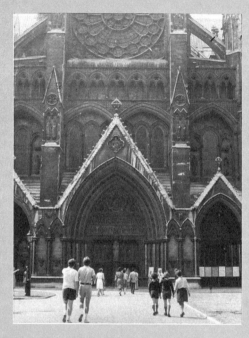

IN MEMORY OF
ROBERT BADEN-POWELL
CHIEF SCOUT OF THE WORLD
1857 — 1941

6.
STANHOPE TERRACE, W2: The whole of this street has been pulled down and re-built since B.-P. was born at what was No. 6 on the 22nd February, 1857. If you wish to visit it you will see how close it is to Hyde Park where, as a boy, young Robert spent many happy hours playing and learning about life in the outdoors with his mother, brothers and sisters.

5.
LONDON SKETCH CLUB, 7 Dilke Street, SW3: One of B.-P.'s many talents was his ability as an artist – sketching, drawing and painting. He was an active member of this Club for several years.

7.
ST. JAMES'S CHURCH, Sussex Gardens, W2:
This is not far from Stanhope Terrace and is where
B.-P. was baptised on 8th July, 1857. He was
christened Robert Stephenson Smyth Powell – his
first two names in honour of his godfather Robert
Stephenson, who was the son of George
Stephenson, the famous nineteenth century
engineer and railway pioneer.

8.
HYDE PARK GATE, SW7: On the south side of
Hyde Park you'll find a cul-de-sac called Hyde Park
Gate. B.-P. lived at No. 9 between 1861 and 1878.
As you can see from the picture, there's an 'official'
plaque on the wall.

9.
BADEN-POWELL HOUSE, QUEEN'S GATE,
SW7: Although B.-P. never lived or worked here, he
must have passed this site many times on his travels
around London. Soon after he died in 1941, the next
Chief Scout (Lord Somers) announced that he
would like to see one of B.-P.'s most earnest dreams
come true – that there should be a Scout house in
London, the City where the Founder had been born,
and the capital of the country where Scouting
started. Lord Somers died in 1944, but his idea lived
on. In 1956 The Scout Association bought the
bomb-damaged corner site. In 1959 the Foundation
Stone was laid and a new building began to rise

rapidly from the ground. On 12th July 1961 Her
Majesty The Queen officially opened the House . . .
and since then thousands of members and friends of
the Movement have passed sculptor Don Potter's
granite figure of B.-P. and through the glass doors
. . . to stay the night . . . to attend a meeting . . . to
have a meal . . .
Michael and David were particularly interested in
'The Baden-Powell Story', a permanent exhibition
in words, sounds and pictures. Here you can see
them looking at the part about the first Scout Camp
on Brownsea Island in 1907, and at B.-P.'s
collection of walking sticks.

10.
SCOUT HEADQUARTERS, Cromwell Road, SW7: The administrative departments of Scout Headquarters moved into this fine new building, next door to Baden-Powell House, in May 1976. It was officially opened by Her Majesty The Queen on 24th November 1976.

The Pound and the Paper Clips

by Eric Franklin

This trick is best performed with a £1 note so if there is a grown-up around ask if you can borrow one. If not, use a piece of paper of similar texture and size. You also need two ordinary wire paper clips.

Fold the note or piece of paper into three but do not crease the folds. Push on the two paper clips as shown in the first two drawings on the left. Now, take hold of the two free corners between the fingers and thumbs and pull the note out straight: do this smartly, not slowly. The two clips will fly off, but instead of being two separate paper clips, they will have mysteriously joined together.

P. J. Stuckey LSIA gives you some information about

AVIATION THROUGH THE AGES

1.
This is a hot air balloon designed by the Frenchman, Montgolfier, in 1783. It was made with cotton and lined with paper. In the same year a hydrogen balloon was flown at Versailles by Professor Charles.

2.
The earliest successful experiments in heavier-than-air manned flight were carried out on hang-gliders. The German Otto Lilienthal was one of the most prominent pioneers. He designed both monoplane and biplane gliders. One of his monoplanes is shown in the illustration. Lilienthal lost his life while testing one of these gliders.

3.
France was the first European country to give official encouragement to the pioneers of aviation. The Frenchman Louis Blériot made the first successful air crossing of the English Channel in 1909. He flew a monoplane of his own design from Calais to Dover in $36\frac{1}{2}$ minutes.

4.
During the 1914-1918 War the rigid airship had been developed for long range bombing. After the War this experience was used in the field of civil passenger transport. In 1924 work began on the design of two airships – the R.100 which was a private venture, and the R.101 which was sponsored by the government. The R.100 was designed by Dr. Barnes Wallis and was completely successful.
In the summer of 1930 the R.100 flew to Canada and back almost without incident. Later in the same year the government insisted that their R.101 should fly to India, even though it was known that she was not ready for such a long journey. All but six of those on board died when she hit a hillside and was destroyed by fire at Beauvais on October 5th 1930. This brought to an end the development of a rigid airship in Great Britain, and the highly successful R.100 was broken up at Cardington in 1931.

5.
In May 1927 an American pilot, Charles A. Lindbergh, became the first airman to fly solo, non-stop, from New York to Paris, a distance of some 3,610 miles. His aircraft was a Ryan monoplane, powered by a 237 h.p. Wright Whirlwind engine, fitted with an enormous petrol tank forward of the cabin, and a periscope so that he could see over the top of the tank.

6.
Of all the single-seat fighters of World War II (1939-1945) the Supermarine Spitfire and the Hawker Hurricane must be the most famous. Both were powered with the Rolls Royce Merlin engine, although the later Mark Spitfires were fitted with the Rolls Royce Griffon engine. Like the Hurricane, the Spitfire remained a front line fighter throughout the War and well into the 1950s, being up-dated and modified to suit different requirements. The one illustrated is an aircraft of No. 19 Squadron, which was stationed at Duxford during the Battle of Britain in 1940.

7.
In 1945 the world's first jet-propelled fighter, the German Messerschmitt Me 262A-1a, went into squadron service. Its maximum speed of 540 m.p.h. was much faster than the best propeller-driven fighters, but Germany's fuel shortage, and the fact that Hitler insisted on using it as a bomber instead of a fighter, prevented its potential being used before the war ended.

8.
The de Havilland Comet was the world's first jet airliner to enter passenger airline service. It was first shown to the public in 1949 and is still seeing service with many of the world's airlines today. The Comet and its Bristol counterpart, the turbo-prop 'Britannia', were the last big aircraft to have engines and airframes produced by the same Company.

9.
Britain and France share the honour of producing the world's first supersonic airliner to go into regular passenger service – the Concorde. With its four Rolls Royce Bristol Olympus engines it can fly at more than twice the speed of sound. The Russians have developed a similar aircraft for use, at present, on internal air routes. It is so much like the Concorde that it has been nicknamed the 'Concordski'.

10.
In August 1970, No. 4 Squadron of the Royal Air Force became the first military unit in the world to use fixed wing V/STOL (Vertical or Short Take-Off and Landing) combat aircraft anywhere outside Britain. It is the Hawker Siddeley Harrier, which is also in service with the United States Marine Corps.

11.
During the last twenty years the helicopter has become a very important part of the air scene – both civil and military. The Westland-Aerospatiale SA 330E 'Puma' is a very advanced and powerful example of Anglo-French achievement in this field, and serves with No. 33 Squadron of the Royal Air Force.

12.
The airship 'Europa' belongs to the Good Year Company. It is one of the non-rigid types, having no internal framework. It was constructed in the old airship sheds at Cardington in 1972. She is the first powered lighter-than-air craft to be seen in British skies since 1930, but now appears at many major outdoor events during the summer.

13.
If the re-appearance of the airship has put the clock back, then an even earlier concept of aviation has put it back still further with the current revival of hang-gliding. However, unlike the gliders of the early pioneers, the modern hang-glider is scientifically designed to known aerodynamic principles.

14.
The story of aviation has come full circle with the hot air balloon, except that now the balloon takes its source of heat with it in the form of a propane torch. A modern hot air balloon is capable of remaining airborne for a considerable time and so popular a sport is it that brightly coloured envelopes can often be seen floating silently across the summer landscape.
Cub Scout Annual

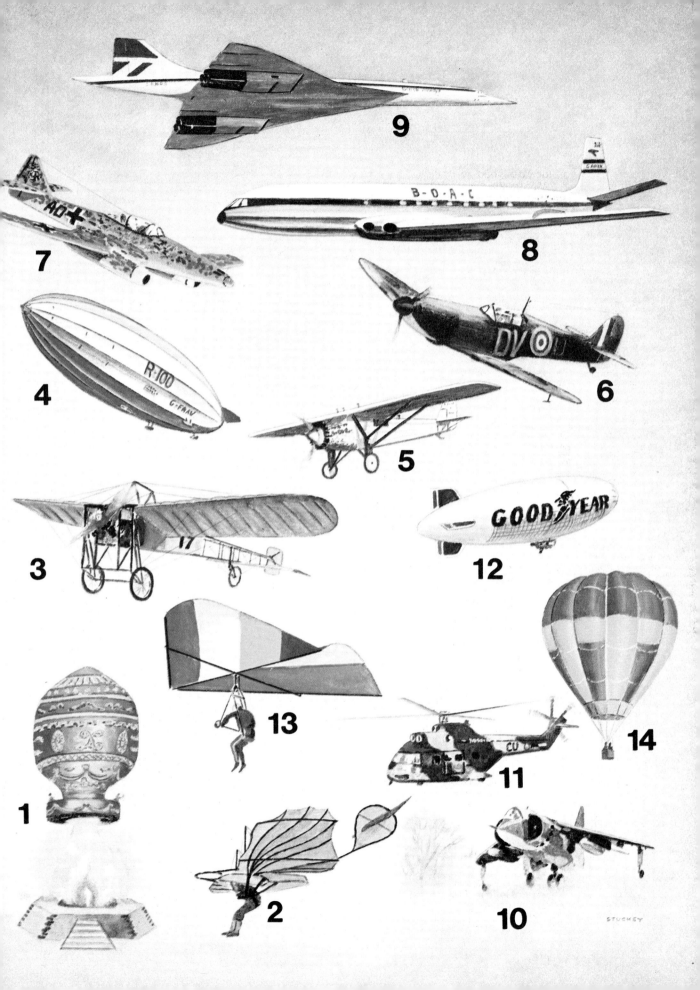

9

B-O-A-C 8

7

6

R-100 4

5

3

GOOD YEAR 12

13

1

11

14

2

10

STUCKEY

What to look for at an Airfield

by Peter Stuckey LSIA

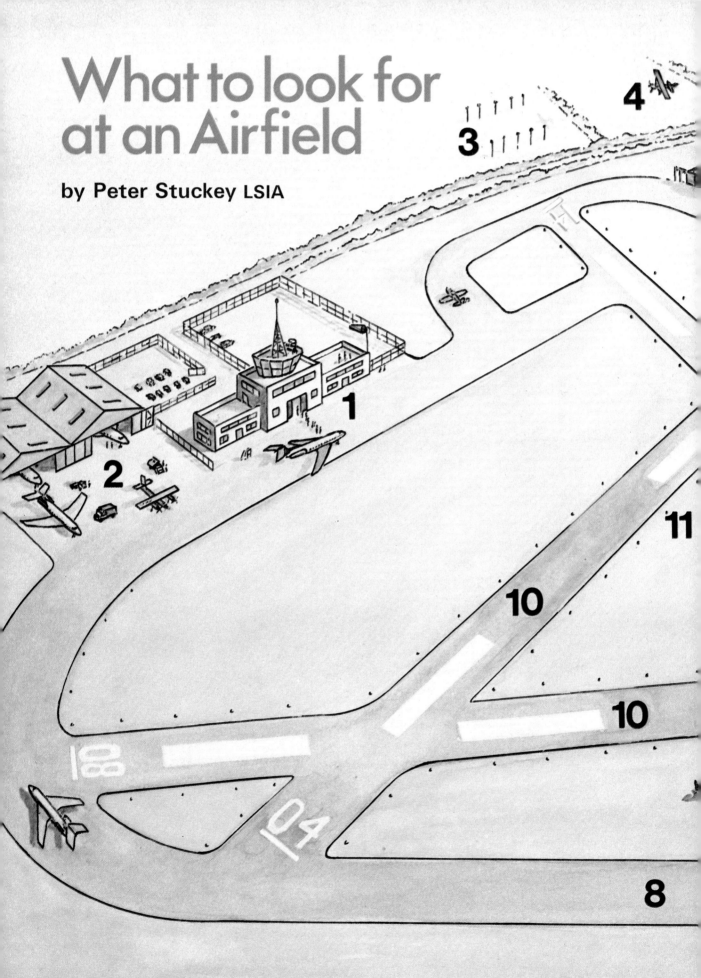

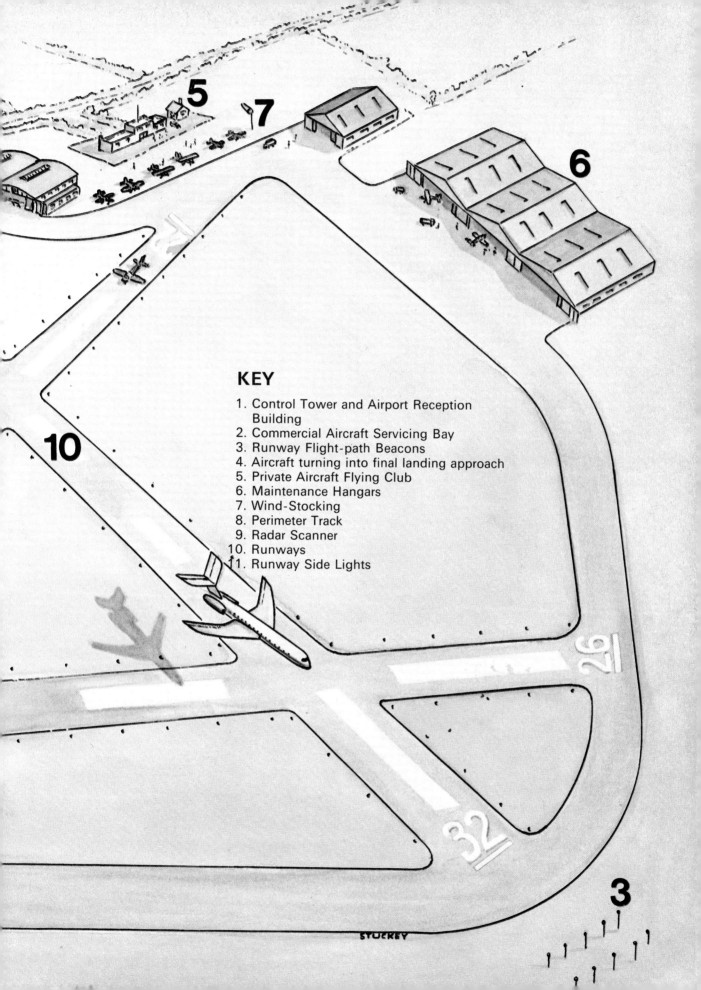

5

7

6

10

KEY

1. Control Tower and Airport Reception Building
2. Commercial Aircraft Servicing Bay
3. Runway Flight-path Beacons
4. Aircraft turning into final landing approach
5. Private Aircraft Flying Club
6. Maintenance Hangars
7. Wind-Stocking
8. Perimeter Track
9. Radar Scanner
10. Runways
11. Runway Side Lights

26

32

3

STUCKEY

be a wildlife detective

Some hints about camouflage, stalking and observation by David Harwood

It's much more exciting to see a badger emerging from its set, a bird on its nest feeding its young, or a hare playing with its leverets with your own eyes than it is to read about them in books or to watch a film about them on television. Of course, you could always go to a zoo, but that's very tame compared with seeking them out yourself 'in the wild' in their natural surroundings.

Successful stalking and observation means using at least four of your five senses – sight, touch, hearing and smell. Your Cub Scout training will help you sharpen your senses: this is most important because animals will use *their* senses. They have to . . . to survive.

Camouflage

You will need to camouflage yourself so that you can see without being seen. This will mean taking three things into account – your location, your clothes and yourself.

The location: Carefully use the natural materials (leaves, grass, plants, etc.) around you to hide yourself, and to break up the outline of your body. Use as little of the material as you can to the greatest effect. Do not forget to change your camouflage when you move from one type of location to another, otherwise you may be seen more easily than if you had not tried to camouflage yourself at all!

1. Simple camouflage in a country setting – note the hat which blends in with the background.

2. Bad camouflage! This stalker can be seen very easily because he has made no use of natural materials, is wearing the wrong clothes (particularly the white vest), and has lots of pink skin visible . . . not to mention his ginger hair!

3. The wrong camouflage – nowhere within a hundred yards are there leaves like these.

Your clothes: These should be of a similar colour to the main colours of the location in which you are operating. As you will not be able to take a suitcase for a change of clothes, wear old clothes of neutral colours (for example, browns and greens), or, particularly in the early morning or evening, black. You should be able to walk, creep or crawl easily, so make sure your clothes fit you snugly, as loose ones may catch or snag in brambles, branches or bushes. For your own protection as well as to keep you hidden wear socks, *long* trousers and have something to put over your head. Avoid wearing anything shiny which may reflect the light and give you away.

4. The green clothes being worn here match the colours of the woodland in which this Cub Scout is operating.

5. Do not wear anything shiny which, as you can see here, *will* reflect the light.

6. 'Natural' make-up is the best way of camouflaging yourself. This Cub Scout is using mud . . . .

Yourself: Any exposed skin like your hands, face and neck should be camouflaged. Mum might let you have some of her mascara or eye shadow, but natural materials like earth or charcoal are just as good (if not better), cheaper, and will wash off with soap and water.

7. . . . whereas this Cub has used powdered charcoal mixed with water.

8. There *is* a Cub Scout under this tree! He has used the cover of the foliage and the shadow . . .

Take Cover

However good your camouflage, you will need to be able to keep out of sight both when you are stalking and when you are staying in one place. Here are some tips.

Make use of natural cover: Avoid open areas, high ground and ridges. Ditches, hedges, outcrops of rocks, boulders, depressions, mounds, trees, bushes, etc. all provide places where you can keep out of sight.

Don't look up!: Always look round the side of your 'shield'. If you look over the top, you are much more likely to be spotted.

10.. Do not look over the top of your cover . . .

11. . . . but keep hidden and look round the side (and look what a difference wearing some suitable headgear makes).

9. You can now see where he is when he shows his hand.

Keep the main source of light in front of you: If the light source (the sun or the moon) is behind you, particularly at dawn or dusk, your silhouette will stand out in sharp relief against the brighter background.

12. Your silhouette will stand out against a light background . . .

13. . . . so keep your head down (I had to ask this Cub Scout to lift his head a little in order that you could see where he was).

Keep below whatever you are stalking: If you are half way up a slope, particularly if it is a steep one, and whatever you are stalking (which is called a 'quarry') is farther down the slope, your outline will still be visible, even though you are not on the crest of the ridge.

By the way, an animal's eyesight will sometimes be better than yours. Many nocturnal creatures can see much better than you, so take extra care at dawn, dusk and night.

14. These three pictures and the diagram show the importance of
15. keeping *below* your quarry when you are stalking along or
16. around a slope. The Cub Scout stayed in exactly the same place while I photographed him from below (down the slope) (14), where you can see him; from up the slope (where the quarry would be) (15) where he is invisible until he raises his arm so you can see where he is (16).

PICTURES 15. AND 16. TAKEN HERE

QUARRY

STALKER

PICTURE 14, TAKEN FROM HERE

Moving about

As a wildlife detective you'll have to know not only about camouflage and taking cover, but also about moving through the countryside. Probably the nearest that you, as a human being, ever come to 'free movement' is when you're swimming. In the water you can move about smoothly in all directions. On land it's virtually impossible to attain free movement. So, as a stalker you're presented with quite a challenge: you need to travel with the maximum care, and the minimum of noise and disturbance.

17. The right way of walking, putting the foot down flat and using the arms to maintain balance.

18. Crawling – the wrong way! Do not imagine that you'll be hidden if your hands and feet are near to, or on, the ground!

19. . . . Lie flat!

Walking: Where there's plenty of natural cover, you should be able to walk relatively easily, but you'd be wise to note these points:

*Keep your balance . . . place your foot flatly and carefully on the ground, *not* toes or heels first, but the sole and heel together. Do not move one foot forward until the other is firmly on the ground. Use your arms to trim your balance just like a gymnast.

*Develop a smooth, rhythmic movement so that you can, if necessary, 'freeze'. You should be able to stop naturally at any time with your muscles relaxed. You will not be able to keep a motionless position for long if your muscles are tensed up.

*Watch where you are going, so that you don't trip up or put your foot on a dry or dead stick which might snap and startle your quarry.

Crossing open country: There will be occasions when there will be little or no cover and you will not be able to completely hide yourself. You can keep your 'exposure' as little as possible by crawling, which means . . .

*Lie as close to the ground as possible, and that means *all* of you! It's no use having your head and feet low if your bottom is stuck up in the air making a very obvious landmark!

*Move carefully, feeling the way in front of you with your hands, letting your knees and feet follow in the places where your hands have already cleared a 'safe' path.

*Avoid jerky movements and, as with walking, be prepared to freeze and lie low at any time.

Feeling the way

I've already mentioned your sense of touch when you're crawling across open country. Your sense of touch will be very important when you're in deep shadow or when it's dark. Just as a blind person uses his hands as eyes when reading Braille, so you can use your fingers as sensors to feel your way round any obstacle in your path. So camouflage your hands rather than wearing gloves.

You do smell!

Although you will not often use your sense of smell when stalking wildlife, everyone and everything does have a distinctive smell – including you! Many animals and birds have very sensitive 'noses'. Even in a light breeze your smell can be carried a long way, so if you are in a position where the wind is blowing *from* you towards your quarry, you will give him warning of your presence. Therefore you should always try and stalk with the wind in your face (known as 'working up wind') so that your smell is blown harmlessly away. The wind will carry sounds too. Sometimes, therefore, you may have to go on a circular detour to avoid alerting an animal, but the extra time and effort will be well worth while because once alerted, your quarry is likely to run away and be on the lookout for you later.

If you are not sure which way the wind is blowing, there are a number of simple ways of finding out. As Robert Baden-Powell (the Founder of Scouting, who was himself an expert stalker) wrote in *Scouting for Boys:* 'Wet your thumb all round with your tongue, and then hold it up and see which side feels the coldest, or you can throw some light dust, or dry grass or leaves in the air and see which way they drift!'

Keep quiet and listen

Sounds can travel a long way in the country, so don't carry anything which will rattle or chink (for example, keys or money) and watch out for those dry sticks or twigs. Breathe as quietly as you can — always through your nose rather than your mouth. Don't talk to your friends unless it's vital — devise a system or code of silent signalling instead.

Stalking and watching wildlife is an absorbing and fascinating experience, but please remember these 'rules' . . .

1. Never touch or disturb the wildlife you observe and stalk, and keep the whole of the Country Code.

2. Never go stalking alone (not until you are quite a lot older anyway), and always tell an adult where you are going and how long you expect to be.

3. Do not go on private land without permission.

4. Make sure you keep warm and dry.

20. Testing the wind direction by throwing up a handful of dust.

21. When you're observing wildlife at close quarters, be camouflaged, lie flat, and keep quiet.

having fun

**It's great to be a Cub Scout!
These pictures show just a few
of the ways in which
Cub Scouts enjoy themselves.**

photographs by Laurie Curtis

Space hopper racing . . .

'Slippery pole' contest . . .

Going over an obstacle course . . .

Most of you will either have – or would like to have – a pet. Pets, like people, need special care, food and attention. In this feature L. HUGH NEWMAN, the well known naturalist and author of many books including *How's Your Pet?* and *Pets for Pleasure and Profit* gives you some notes about . . .

POPULAR PETS

Illustrated by Glenn Rix

The Dog Dogs hate to be left alone and so, if you decide to make a pet of one, you must give him plenty of attention and take him for regular walks. Never allow him to roam about alone, either in the country or in a town, and make sure he always wears a collar with your name and address on it. Train him to be obedient by praising him when he does what you ask, and never use a stick to hit him when he does wrong as it could turn him into a savage animal. Make sure he has regular meals, feed a puppy four times a day, but a fully grown dog only once. Your dog will need meat and biscuits mixed with some uncooked green vegetables and fresh water to drink at all times. All young dogs must be innoculated against distemper by a vet.

The Cat A cat is a very independent creature and likes to go its own way. Most cats, with the exception of the Siamese breed, don't mind being alone as long as they get their food regularly, but they do like their owners to stroke and cuddle them now and then, when *they* feel like it, and they must have a warm sleeping place out of draughts. All cats are fussy over their food, and although some will eat tinned cat food others will only eat fresh meat (being especially fond of liver) and, of course, fish. They all like milk to drink. Young kittens are very playful, but they also need a lot of sleep while they are growing, so don't disturb them when they are resting, and that goes for a fully grown cat too!

The Rabbit A rabbit can quite easily be tamed if you give it plenty of attention and love. It should be kept in a roomy hutch out of the draughts, with plenty of dry straw or hay for bedding, and this should be changed every few days. Give your rabbit root vegetables like carrots, turnips and parsnips to eat and also oats or bran, crusts of stale brown bread and some green food such as dandelion, or thistle leaves, even fresh green grass, and from the garden cabbage leaves and carrot tops. It is a good idea to let all this green food wilt in the sun for a few hours before feeding to your pet so that it does not get a stomach upset from too fresh green stuff. If your garden is well fenced in, it is quite safe to let your rabbit have a run on the lawn now and then and the exercise will do him good.

The Stick Insect These odd looking insects are very easy pets to keep but you do need some kind of cage in which they will get light and air. A simple framework covered with muslin or mosquito netting will do, or you could use a roomy cardboard carton with a muslin top. The ordinary stick insect needs no other food but privet leaves, so all you have to do is to pick a bunch of privet shoots every few days and stand these in the cage in a jam jar of water. Clean out the cage once a week, and if you want to have more stick insects gather up the barrel shaped eggs from the bottom of the cage and put them in a separate box to hatch.

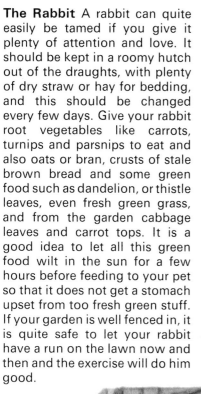

The Hamster A Golden Hamster is a very amusing pet to have but you must learn to handle it very gently or it may bite you. It should be kept in a proper strong hamster cage from which it cannot gnaw its way out. A sleeping compartment should be well filled with soft hay and if you put a small metal tray filled with sawdust in one corner of the cage the hamster will use this for its droppings and it will be very easy to keep the place clean. Don't keep more than one hamster in a cage or they will fight. Hamsters are small eaters but they like a very mixed diet of cereals, vegetables, fruit, nuts, seeds and even small insects!

The Goldfish You can keep goldfish either in an aquarium tank or in a pond out of doors, but a goldfish bowl is not a suitable container. There must be green weeds in the water to provide oxygen and water snails to act as scavengers and keep the bottom of the tank clean. In a small aquarium you will also have to change the water from time to time when it gets cloudy. Fish should not be over fed, and in hot weather and during the winter they need very little food. You can buy fish food in packets and also live food such as water fleas from pet shops. Goldfish also like greenfly and small worms.

The Pigeon Pigeons are perfectly hardy birds and can be kept out of doors in a dovecote or a pigeon loft. It is best to get a pair and shut them up for a few days before you allow them to fly free. They should be fed on pigeon corn, which you can buy from pet shops. They also like some green food like lettuce leaves, clover and chickweed or cabbage. Clean water and grit is also very important and the drinking bowl must be washed every day. The house, and especially the ledges where the birds sleep, should be swept down every few days.

The Budgerigar These pretty birds are best kept indoors in a cage if you only have a single one, or it will be lonely. Pairs are quite happy in an outdoor aviary as long as they can find shelter from cold weather and rain. They should be fed on budgerigar mixture, which you can buy, and they also like to peck at sprays of millet and seeding grasses. In the winter they need a little codliver oil on their food, and they should always have fresh water and grit. You must clean out the cage regularly and keep the floor sprinkled with sand. A tame budgerigar can be allowed to fly about the room now and then, but make sure the windows are closed.

The Parrot Parrots like company and if you get one as a pet it is a good idea to put its cage near a window where it can see people coming and going. Give your parrot plenty of attention and try to teach it to talk. It also needs something to play with – like cotton reels, clothes pegs and corks – or it may become bored and begin to pick out its own feathers. Feed it on parrot seed, nuts, fruit, biscuits and hard rusks as well as some green food, and always remember to clean out and re-fill the drinking bowl each day. Like all birds, parrots also need grit to help digest their food.

The Tortoise A tortoise is the sort of pet you can allow to roam freely round the garden if you know that it is properly fenced so that it cannot escape. It will then find its own food, nibbling here and there as it fancies. If this is not possible then you must keep your tortoise in an enclosure of some kind, with a little hutch or box for sleeping in, and feed it on lettuce and cabbage leaves, slices of carrot and apple, bits of tomato or even strawberries if you can spare them. In the autumn when the tortoise becomes sleepy and wants to hibernate it should be packed down into a box filled with straw or leaves and stored in a cool frost-proof place until the spring.

The Mouse Tame mice are easy pets to look after and if you get a pair you will soon have a great many more. They should be kept in a proper cage or mouse-house where there is plenty of room to run about. Put a layer of sawdust on the floor and fix a drinking bottle to the wall. You can get one of these from a pet shop. There should also be a nesting box filled with hay. The best food is a mixture of rolled oats and bird seed and they also like brown bread and a little green stuff, as well as small pieces of apple or carrot, but not cheese. Don't leave stale food in the cage, and clean it often or it will begin to smell unpleasant.

Peter Harrison describes the

Village Pond

Hundreds of years ago the village pond was a watering place for travellers' horses, and for cattle and livestock on their way to or from market. You are unlikely to see this nowadays, but in many parts of the country the village pond remains.

Each pond is unique. Some ponds are well looked after, others have become overgrown. Each has hundreds, if not thousands, of different kinds of life living in, on or around its water. The 'permanent residents' are usually very hardy, having to survive through freezing winters, spring and autumn rains, and perhaps a summer drought. Others are 'temporary residents' only to be found at certain times of the year.

Some, like the small, brilliantly coloured kingfisher or the majestic bulrush, are relatively easy to identify. Others, like the water stick insect, which breathes through a tube from the water's surface, are so small or so well camouflaged that you will need patience, practice and a reference book to discover what they are.

In this picture you can see just twenty-one plants and creatures which you might find round about a pond. There are many, many more . . . if you look, listen and observe.

There are two other features in this Annual which you will find helpful when exploring a pond – the Waterscope (page 33), and Stalking and Camouflage (page 44). Also remember always to take great care of yourself near water, and always follow the Country Code (see page 56)).

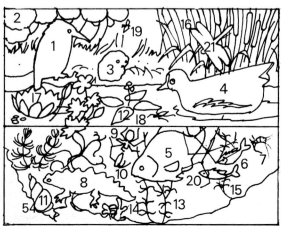

KEY

1. Kingfisher
2. Alder
3. Water Vole
4. Moorhen
5. Carp
6. Sticklebacks
7. Freshwater Shrimp
8. Great Crested Newt
9. Water Spider
10. Whirligig Beetle
11. Great Pond Snail
12. Water Plantain
13. Canadian Pondweed
14. Freshwater Sponge
15. Water Crowfoot
16. Bulrush
17. White Water-Lily
18. Pond Skater
19. House Martins
20. Water Stick Insect
21. Emperor Dragon Fly

Nature PHOTO·QUIZ

Here's a chance for you to test your nature knowledge. Look carefully at each photograph and then answer the question about it. Try hard to get all the answers before looking at the solution on page 62.

1. What insects are these, and what are they doing?
2. What animal is this? How old do you think it is?
3. Which reptile's head is this?
4. What mammal is this? Where is its natural habitat?
5. What is this? Is it poisonous?
6. What snake is this?
7. What is this?

photographs by Roy Harris

1

2

3

5

4

Monty Ball's Handmade Shoes

written and photographed by John Slip

A hundred years ago there were no cars. People travelled by road on horseback or in horse-drawn coaches. As horses need shoes to protect their hooves, there were smiths' forges all over the country. As the car and other methods of transport replaced the horse, so the number of blacksmiths – smiths who work with iron – and farriers – who are shoeing-smiths – became fewer. However, as long as people ride horses for work, sport or pleasure, the farrier's craft will not die.

Like his grandfather and father before him, Mr. Monty Ball is a farrier and a blacksmith. These pictures show what patience, care and skill is needed to give a horse a new set of shoes.

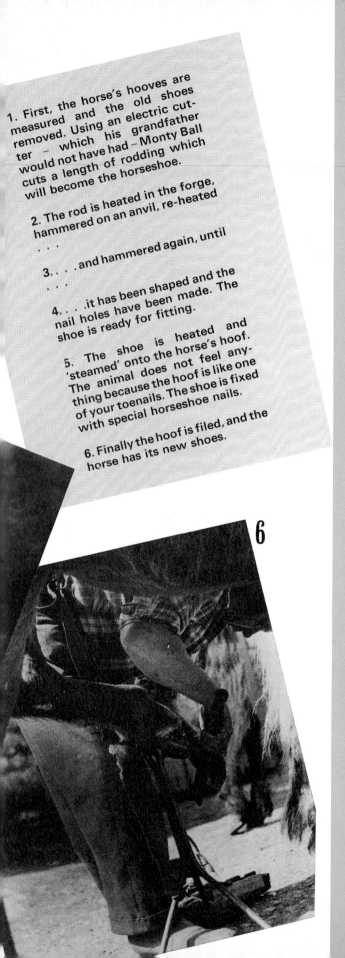

1. First, the horse's hooves are measured and the old shoes removed. Using an electric cutter — which his grandfather would not have had – Monty Ball cuts a length of rodding which will become the horseshoe.

2. The rod is heated in the forge, hammered on an anvil, re-heated . . .

3. . . . and hammered again, until . . .

4. . . . .it has been shaped and the nail holes have been made. The shoe is ready for fitting.

5. The shoe is heated and 'steamed' onto the horse's hoof. The animal does not feel anything because the hoof is like one of your toenails. The shoe is fixed with special horseshoe nails.

6. Finally the hoof is filed, and the horse has its new shoes.

6

The Tramps and the Chickens
by Eric Franklin

All you will need are seven matches or counters.

Take a match in each hand and state that these are two tramps. Place the other five on the table and state that they are five chickens which the tramps had just spotted in a farmyard. Looking round carefully (you must act this) the tramps jumped and grabbed the chickens one by one. Just as they had done so, they heard the farmer coming, and quickly put the chickens back on the ground.

You, of course, picked up the five matches one by one with either hand alternately and then quickly put them back.

The farmer, seeing nothing suspicious, went away, and the tramps grabbed the chickens again one by one. Unfortunately, the chickens squawked and the farmer dashed back.

"What's going on here?" he yelled. "Where are my chickens? Who's over there?"

"It's only us two poor blokes," came the reply.

Open one hand and show just two matches.

"Your chickens are over there."

Open the other hand and show the other five matches.

This is how you do it. When the matches are picked up the first time, the *right* hand picks up the first match; when you put them down again, the *left* hand puts down the first match. The left hand is now empty but you keep it closed as if it still held a match and the right hand contains two matches. When you pick them up again, begin with the *right* hand. This will ensure that you have two matches only in the left hand and five in the right.

59

True or false? Fact or fiction? Sometimes you can never be quite sure, particularly where legends are concerned. And the older the legend, the more versions there are likely to be. GEOFFREY HEMMING tells you his story about . . .

The man who loved the rain

Illustrated by Annabel Spenceley

Do you like the rain or does it bother you? I know it can be a great nuisance when it arrives during the summer holidays when you've planned a visit to the beach or a walk in the countryside. Even worse when it arrives on Guy Fawkes night!

But believe it or not there once lived a man who loved the rain so much that he became its Patron Saint. His name was Swithin.

He was born into a very humble family in Wessex round about 805 A.D. When he was very young he was sent to study at the monastery of Winchester where the kindly monks taught him grammar, philosophy and the Holy Scriptures. Later, when a man, he was ordained by the Bishop of Winchester and eventually became the spiritual director to Egbert, the King of the West Saxons.

In 836 A.D. King Egbert died and his son Ethelwulf succeeded him. But the new king was of a pious and retiring character and was only too delighted to leave the responsibilities of his kingdom in the trustworthy hands of St. Swithin.

In spite of his great power St. Swithin never abused his influence for financial gain. Never once did he forget the poverty of his childhood and throughout his life he remained humble. He was loved and deeply respected by all who knew him.

Many miracles are credited to him, but the most popular one occurred on the bridge he built over the Itchen. St. Swithin was on his way to church one morning when he came upon an old woman in great distress.

Nearby lay an upturned basket, and about her feet were smashed eggs which she had intended to sell at market. Without saying a word, St. Swithin knelt before her and picked up the broken egg-shells. When he placed them in her basket the eggs were whole again.

Growing older and knowing full well that his death was not far away, St. Swithin made it known that when he died he wanted to be buried out in the grounds of Winchester Cathedral where the rain could wash the grass that would grow on his grave.

His wish was granted and for many years his tomb was exposed to all weathers. But 108 years after his death, when Winchester Cathedral had been rebuilt, the monks, wishing to pay homage to the great saint, removed his remains and reburied them *inside* the Cathedral.

The date was 15th July, 970 A.D. That same day the sky darkened and the thunderous clouds burst. Rain poured down and it continued for 40 days and 40 nights. Those who witnessed the great deluge believed it was St. Swithin's way of showing his displeasure at being buried indoors.

Legend has it that if it rains on July 15th every year we'll know that the saint who loved the rain is still angry at being buried indoors and out of reach of the raindrops.

ALL ABOUT THE WEATHER CROSSWORD

By Daphne Pilcher

CLUES ACROSS

1. A sudden blast of wind (4)
5. Dangerous type of ice on roads (5)
7. A block of ice in the sea (4)
8. A cloud – – – – – describes a sudden downpour of rain (5)
9. You expect lots of these in March (5)
11. Misty appearance in the air often due to heat (4)
14. Don't – – – – – under a tree in a thunderstorm (5)
15. When it's this temperature or less it's freezing (4)
16. Thick mist (3)
17. A light, fleecy piece of snow (5)
18. Luminous body around which the earth revolves (3)
19. Sort of storm you might get in a desert (4)
20. Stifling or very humid (5)
22. Sound water might make at a waterfall after heavy rain (4)
23. What the ground is like after a period of no rain (5)
26. Melting snow (5)
27. Winds from this compass direction are usually cold (1, 1 – abbreviation)
28. In this sort of wind you want to wrap up well (4)
29. In the bleak mid-winter, water is 'hard as – – – – –' (5)
30. A sun – – – – can indicate the time in summer weather (4)

CLUES DOWN

2. Whirlwind (7)
3. Moisture falling to the ground (4)
4. What we hope it will be in summer (3)
6. Hot and damp (5)
9. You tend to become this when out in the rain (3)
10. Keep in this if you want to keep cool (5)
12. If the frost is not in the air, it is this sort (6)
13. A heavy downpour (6)
14. Buildings do this in an earthquake (5)
17. An excess of water (5)
19. Some folk bring this back from holiday to forecast the weather (7)
20. Adjective used to describe a bright but fresh Autumn day (5)
21. Opposite to 9 down (3)
24. Crystals of condensed and frozen vapour (4)
25. On the Beaufort Wind Scale this number describes a storm (3)
26. Do this in the shade in hot weather (3)

ANSWERS

This Year's COMPETITION

The Prizes
1st Prize .... £25 of Premium Bonds.
2nd Prize .... Books to the value of £10.
3rd Prize .... Books to the value of £5.
10 Runners-Up Prizes of a book each.

You could win £25 of Premium Bonds in this year's great competition.

Here's what you have to do

1.
On the opposite page there are pictures of objects photographed from unusual angles. First you need to identify accurately each object.
2.
Choose *one* of the objects and use it as part of a 'doodle', drawing or cartoon.
3.
List the three items which you most enjoyed in the 1978 Cub Scout Annual.
4.
Your competition entry can be on any colour, size or shape of paper or card, but must include (in BLOCK CAPITALS) your Name, Date of Birth, Address and Pack.
5.
Send your entry, by 28 February 1978, to:
Cub Scout Annual '78 Competition,
Baden-Powell House,
Queen's Gate,
LONDON, SW7 5JS.

The Rules

1.
All competitors must be under the age of 11 years on 31st December 1977.
2.
The closing date for the competition is 28th February 1978.
3.
The entries will be judged for the following (in this order):
a. the correct identification of the objects.
b. the originality of the 'doodle', drawing or cartoon (taking the age of the competitor into consideration).
4.
The Editor's decision is final. No correspondence can be entered into, and entries cannot be returned.

CUB SCOUT ANNUAL COMPETITION
The objects in the Photoquiz are:

1. ....   7. ....

2. ....   8. ....

3. ....   9. ....

4. ....   10. ....

5. ....   11. ....

6. ....   12. ....

My 'doodle'

The items I most enjoyed are:	From:
1.	Andrew Smith 10 Green Road Anytown
2.	Born 20 April 19— 1st Anytown Pack (Block capitals)
3.	

Answers to Nature Photo-Quiz

1. Wood ants eating a caterpillar which they have caught. 2. A roe deer kid approximately 48 hours old. 3. The head of a giant tortoise. 4. A rhinoceros. Its natural habitat is in Africa and Southern Asia. 5. A slow worm. It is not poisonous. 6. A grass snake. 7. A teasel.

M A N E A T I N G T I G E R S
L O R D O F T H E F L I E S
K I N G O F T H E J E W S
J A C K I N O F F I C E
I N D I G E S T I O N
H O R I Z O N T A L
G R E E T I N G S
F O R E C A S T
E N D O R S E
D E F E N D
C L O W N
B L O W
A N T

Answer to the Great Pyramid Crossword

N O P L A C E L I K E H O M E
O V E R T H E H U R D L E S
P R I N C E O F W A L E S
Q U E E N O F C L U B S
R E C O G N I T I O N
S C O U T C R A F T
T E R R I T O R Y
U N S T E A D Y
V E T E R A N
W O G G L E
X E B E C
Y A N K
Z O O